SCIENCE, LIBERTY AND PEACE

Books *by* ALDOUS HUXLEY

NOVELS
Time Must Have a Stop
After Many a Summer Dies the Swan
Eyeless in Gaza
Point Counter-Point
Those Barren Leaves
Antic Hay
Crome Yellow
Brave New World

ESSAYS AND BELLES LETTRES
Ends and Means
Texts and Pretexts
The Olive Tree
Music at Night
Vulgarity in Literature
Do What You Will
Proper Studies
Jesting Pilate
Along the Road
On the Margin
Essays New and Old
The Art of Seeing
The Perennial Philosophy
Science, Liberty and Peace

SHORT STORIES
Brief Candles
Two or Three Graces
Little Mexican
Mortal Coils
Limbo

BIOGRAPHY
Grey Eminence

POETRY
The Cicadas
Leda

TRAVEL
Beyond the Mexique Bay

DRAMA
The World of Light
The Discovery, adapted from Frances Sheridan

SELECTED WORKS

ROTUNDA

SCIENCE,
LIBERTY AND PEACE

by

Aldous Huxley

Harper & Brothers Publishers

NEW YORK AND LONDON

1 9 4 6

SCIENCE, LIBERTY AND PEACE

"IF THE arrangement of society is bad (as ours is), and a small number of people have power over the majority and oppress it, every victory over Nature will inevitably serve only to increase that power and that oppression. This is what is actually happening."

It is nearly half a century since Tolstoy wrote these words, and what was happening then has gone on happening ever since. Science and technology have made notable advances in the intervening years— and so has the centralization of political and economic power, so have oligarchy and despotism. It need hardly be added that science is not the only causative factor involved in this process. No social evil can possibly have only one cause. Hence the difficulty, in any given case, of finding a complete cure. All that is being maintained here is that progressive science is one of the causative factors involved in the progressive decline of liberty and the progressive centralization of power, which have occurred during the twentieth century.

Applied science touches the lives of individuals and societies at many different points and in a great variety of contexts, and therefore the ways in which it has increased the power of the few over the majority are correspondingly many and various. In the paragraphs that follow I shall enumerate the more obviously significant of these ways, shall indicate how and by what means applied science has contributed hitherto toward the centralization of power in the hands of a small ruling minority, and also how and by what means such tendencies may be resisted and ultimately, perhaps, reversed.

1. In the course of the past two or three generations science and technology have equipped the political bosses who control the various national states with unprecedentedly efficient instruments of coercion. The tank, the flame-thrower and the bomber—to mention but a few of these instruments—have made nonsense of the old techniques of popular revolt. At the same time the recent revolutionary improvements in the means of transport and communications have vastly strengthened the hands of the police. In his own peculiar way, Fouché was a man of first-rate abilities; but compared with the secret

police force at the disposal of a modern dictatorship or even of a modern democracy, the instrument of oppression, which he was able to forge for Napoleon, was an absurdly clumsy piece of machinery. In the past, personal and political liberty depended to a considerable extent upon governmental inefficiency. The spirit of tyranny was always more than willing; but its organization and material equipment were generally weak. Progressive science and technology have changed all this completely. Today, if the central executive wishes to act oppressively, it finds an almost miraculously efficient machine of coercion standing ready to be set in motion. Thanks to the genius and co-operative industry of highly trained physicists, chemists, metallurgists and mechanical inventors, tyrants are able to dragoon larger numbers of people more effectively, and strategists can kill and destroy more indiscriminately and at greater distances, than ever before. On many fronts nature has been conquered; but, as Tolstoy foresaw, man and his liberties have sustained a succession of defeats.

Overwhelming scientific and technological superiority cannot be resisted on their own plane. In 1848 the sporting gun was a match for the muskets of the soldiery, and a barricade made of overturned carts, sandbags and paving stones was a sufficient protection against cavalry and muzzle-loading cannon. After a century of scientific and technological progress no weapons available to the masses of the people can compete with those in the arsenals controlled by the ruling minority. Consequently, if any resistance is to be offered by the many to the few, it must be offered in a field in which technological superiority does not count. In countries where democratic institutions exist and the executive is prepared to abide by the rules of the democratic game, the many can protect themselves against the ruling few by using their right to vote, to strike, to organize pressure groups, to petition the legislature, to hold meetings and conduct press campaigns in favor of reform. But where there are no democratic institutions, or where a hitherto democratic government declines any longer to abide by the rules of the game, a majority which feels itself oppressed may be driven to resort to direct action. But since science and technology, in conquering nature have thereby enormously increased the military and police power of the ruling few, this direct action cannot hope for a successful outcome, if it is violent; for in any armed conflict, the side which has the tanks, planes and flame-throwers cannot fail to defeat the side which is armed at the very best only with small arms and hand grenades.

Is there any way out of the unfavorable political situation in which, thanks to applied science, the masses now find themselves? So far only one hopeful issue has been discovered. In South Africa and, later, in India, Gandhi and his followers were confronted by an oppressive government armed with overwhelming military might. Gandhi, who is not only an idealist and a man of principle, but also an intensely practical politician, attempted to cope with this seemingly desperate situation by organizing a nonviolent form of direct action, which he called *satyagraha*. For a full account of the methods and results of *satyagraha* the reader is referred to *War without Violence* by Krishnalal Shridharani. New York, 1939. Here it is only necessary to state that the method achieved a number of striking successes against odds which, from a military point of view, were overwhelmingly great. To those who think that the record of Gandhi's achievements is irrelevant to the historical and psychological situation of the indus-

[5]

trial West, Mr. Shridharani makes the following answer:

My contact with the Western world has led me to think that, contrary to popular belief, *satyagraha*, once consciously and deliberately adopted, has more fertile fields in which to grow and flourish in the West than in the Orient. Like war, *satyagraha* demands public spirit, self-sacrifice, organization and discipline for its successful operation, and I have found these qualities displayed in Western communities more than in my own. Perhaps the best craftsmen in the art of violence may still be the most effective wielders of non-violent direct action. It is but a question, in the words of William James, of "opinion-making men seizing historic opportunities"

It is often argued that *satyagraha* cannot work against an organization, whose leaders are prepared to exploit their military superiority without qualm or scruple. And of course this may very well be the case. No more than any other form of political action, violent or otherwise, can *satyagraha* guarantee success. But even though, against an entirely ruthless and fanatical opponent, non-co-operation and what Thoreau called "civil disobedience," coupled with a disciplined willingness to accept and even to court sacrificial suffering, may prove unavailing, the resulting situation could not be, materially, any worse than it would have been if the intolerable oppression had been passively accepted or else resisted unavailingly by force; while, psychologically and morally, it would in all probability be very much better—better for those participating in the *satyagraha*, and better in the eyes of spectators and of those who merely heard of the achievement at second hand.

In the years ahead it seems possible that *satyagraha* may take root in the West—not primarily as the result of any "change of heart," but simply because it provides the masses, especially in the conquered countries, with their only practicable form of political action. The Germans of the Ruhr and the Palatinate resorted to *satyagraha* against the French in 1923. The movement was spontaneous; philosophically, ethically and organizationally, it had not been prepared for. It was for this reason that it finally broke down. But it lasted long enough to prove that a Western people—and a people more thoroughly indoctrinated with militarism than any other—was perfectly capable of nonviolent direct action, involving the cheerful acceptance of sacrificial suffering. Similar movements of *satyagraha* (more conscious of themselves this time, and better prepared for) may again be initiated among the masses of conquered Germany. The impracticability of any other kind of political action makes it very possible that this will happen sooner or later. It would be one of the happier ironies of history if the nation which produced Klausewitz and Bernhardi and Hitler were to be forced by circumstances to become the first large-scale exponent in the West of that nonviolent direct action which has become, in this age of scientific progress, humanity's only practical substitute for hopeless revolution and self-stultifying or suicidal war.

2. The pen and the voice are at least as mighty as the sword; for the sword is wielded in obedience to the spoken or the written word. Progressive technology has strengthened the powers that be by providing them not only with bigger and better instruments of coercion, but also with instruments of persuasion incomparably superior to those at the disposal of earlier rulers. The rotary press and, more recently, the radio have contributed greatly to the concentration of political and economic power. James Mill

believed that, when everybody had learned to read, the reign of reason and democracy would be assured forever. But in actual historical fact the spread of free compulsory education, and, along with it, the cheapening and acceleration of the older methods of printing, have almost everywhere been followed by an increase in the power of ruling oligarchies at the expense of the masses. The reasons for this are obvious. A newspaper combining attractiveness with cheapness cannot be produced unless it is subsidized either by advertisers (that is to say, the people who control centralized finance and large-scale, mass-producing and mass-distributing industry), or by some organization desirous, for its own purposes, of influencing public opinion, or by the central government. In countries where the press is said to be free, newspapers are subsidized primarily by advertisers, and to a lesser extent by political parties, financial or professional groups. In countries where the press is not free, newspapers are subsidized by the central government. The man who pays the piper always calls the tune. In capitalist democracies the popular press supports its advertisers by inculcating the benefits of centralized industry and finance, coupled with as much centralized government as will enable these institutions to function at a profit. In totalitarian states all newspapers preach the virtues of governmental omnipotence, one-party politics and state control of everything. In both cases progressive technology has strengthened the hands of the local bosses by providing them with the means of persuading the many that concentration of political and economic power is for the general benefit.

What is true of the press is equally true of the radio. Spoken words are more exciting than words printed on wood pulp. In the past a great orator could reach, at the most, only a few thousand listeners. Today, thanks to applied science, a dictator with a gift of the gab is able to pour his emotionally charged evangel into the ears of tens of millions. What Mark Anthony could do to the mob assembled round Caesar's corpse, his modern counterpart can do to entire nations. Never have so many been so much at the mercy of so few.

Undesirable propaganda will not cease until the persons who pay for propaganda either change their minds, or are replaced by other persons willing to pay for something else. Meanwhile there is no remedy for the evil except personal self-denial. Reading news-papers and listening to the radio are psychological addictions; and psychological addictions, like the physiological addictions to drugs, tobacco and alco-hol, can only be put an end to by a voluntary effort on the part of the addict. So long as people yield to the craving to read about murders and divorces and to look at the comic strips, or to listen to soap operas and swing music, they must expect to be influenced by the propaganda which always accompanies these habit-forming stimuli. A questionnaire on reading habits was recently addressed by the heads of a New York labor union to its membership. Among the questions asked were: What newspaper do you regu-larly read? and what newspaper do you consider the least trustworthy and most untruthful? Sixty per cent of the membership agreed that newspaper X was the most untruthful sheet in the New York area, but over forty per cent admitted to making it their daily read-ing—because of its superior comic strips and more violent sensationalism. As usual, it is a case of *video meliora proboque; deteriora sequor*—I see the better and I approve; but the worse is what I pursue. Under the present dispensation, nothing but self-denial on the part of readers can diminish the influence of newspaper X. Continued indulgence in psychological addictions has to be paid for, and the price is undesirable propaganda.

3. By supplying the ruling oligarchy with more effective instruments of coercion and persuasion, applied science has contributed directly to the centralization of power in the hands of the few. But it has also made important indirect contributions to the same end. It has done this in two ways; first, by introducing over ever larger areas of the industrial and agricultural economy the methods of large-scale mass production and mass distribution; second, by creating, through its very progressiveness, an economic and social insecurity which drives all those concerned, owners and managers no less than workers, to seek the assistance of the national state. Let us now consider these two power-centralizing factors in greater detail.

a) In applying the results of disinterested scientific research, inventors and technicians have paid more attention to the problem of equipping large concerns with the expensive machinery of mass production and mass distribution than to that of providing individuals or co-operating groups with cheap and simple, but effective, means of production for their own subsistence and for the needs of a local market. The reason for this is that there has been more money in working for the mass producers and mass distributors; and the mass producers and mass distributors have had more money because financiers have seen that there was more profit for them, and more power, in a centralized than in a decentralized system of production.

Here, in parenthesis, let us note that concentration of financial power preceded the scientific revolution of the eighteenth and nineteenth centuries and was largely responsible for making our industrial civilization the hateful thing it was and, for the most part, still is. Throughout Europe land and natural resources were not owned outright by the people, represented by a multitude of small holders; nor were they the property of a sovereign, leasing to small tenants and spending the rent (which is the monetary expression of the social value of land) for social purposes. The best part of the land and its natural resources was the monopoly of a small class of landlords, who appropriated the social values of what should, quite obviously, have been everybody's property, to their own private use. Hence the early centralization of financial power—a power that was used to exploit the new technological discoveries for the benefit, not of individual small producers or co-operating groups, but for that of the class, which alone possessed accumulations of money. Centralized finance begot centralized industry, and in due course the profits of centralized industry increased the power of centralized finance, so that it was able to proceed ever further in the direction of completely centralized production and distribution.

The centralizing of industrial capacity in big mass-producing factories has resulted in the centralization of a large part of the population in cities and in the reduction of ever-increasing numbers of individuals to complete dependence upon a few private capitalists and their managers, or upon the one public capitalist, the state, represented by politicians and working through civil servants. So far as liberty is concerned, there is little to choose between the two types of boss. Up to the present, state-controlled enterprises have been closely modeled upon those of capitalist big business. Nationalization has not stopped short at land and natural resources, nor have the land and natural resources been nationalized with the purpose of giving individuals or co-operating groups free access to the means of small-scale production, personal liberty and self-government. On the contrary, the objects nationalized include, besides land and natural resources, the tools of production, and that nationalization has been undertaken with a view to strengthening the state (that is to say, the politicians momentarily in power) against its subjects and not at all with the purpose of liberating individual men and women from economic dependence upon bosses. But economic dependence upon bosses is always bad, because, quite obviously, it is no easily reconcilable with local and professional self-government or with civil and personal liberty. Democratic institutions are likely to work best at times and in places where at least a good part of the citizens have access to enough land and possess sufficient tools and professional skill to be able to provide for their subsistence without recourse to financially potent private capitalists or to the government. Where, as in the contemporary Western world, great numbers of the citizens own nothing (not even, in many cases, a skill, since the operation of semi-automatic machines does not require a skill), personal liberty and political and civil rights are to a more or less considerable extent dependent upon the grace of the capitalistic or national owners and managers of the means of production and distribution, and upon their willingness to abide by the rules of the democratic game. To forward their interests and to protect themselves against oppression, propertyless workers combine in trade unions. These have done much to bridle the ambition and covetousness of capitalists and to improve the conditions of labor. But trade unions are as subject to gigantism and centralization as are the industries to which they are related. Consequently it happens all too frequently that the masses of unionized workers find themselves dependent upon, and subordinated to, two governing oligarchies—that of the bosses and that of the union leaders. Over the first they have no control at all, except by strike and the threat of strike; over the second their control is at best remote and rather shadowy. Self government, which is the very essence of democratic freedom, is more or less completely absent from their professional lives. This is ultimately due, as we have seen, to propertylessness and consequent dependence upon the private or public owners and managers of the means of mass production and mass distribution; and propertylessness is due in its turn to (among other things) the progress of applied science—a progress which, under the auspices of centralized finance, has hitherto favored mass production at the expense of production on a small scale for personal or co-operative use, or to supply a local market.

In the most highly industrialized countries, applied science and its ally, and master, centralized finance, have profoundly changed the traditional pattern of agricultural life. Thus, in the United States, the percentage of the population making its living from the land has been reduced in recent years to only a fifth of the total. Meanwhile the size of individual holdings of land has tended to increase, as powerful corporations add field to field in the effort to exploit mechanized farming to its economic limit. Small-scale farmers, who used to be primarily concerned with subsistence, secondarily with a cash crop, have been largely replaced by men whose primary concern is with cash crops and who use the cash so earned to buy "nationally advertised," processed and denatured foods at the grocers.

In Russia the process of centralizing and consolidating the control of land and of industrializing agricultural production has been carried out by government decree and by means of the liquidation of a whole class of society. It would appear, however, that a measure of small-scale private ownership, or quasi-ownership, has had to be reintroduced in order to increase agricultural efficiency by improving the morale of the workers.

b) Among the ordinary results of the rapid progress of applied science are technological unemployment and the sudden and unexpected necessity of changing long-established habits of agricultural and industrial production. When too rapid, changes of position or state are very disturbing to living organisms, sometimes even fatal. That is why, when we get out of a plane in mid-air, we use a parachute, why, when we take a Turkish bath, we do not plunge immediately into the hottest chamber. Analogously, social, economic and political changes can take place too rapidly and too frequently for human well-being. A highly progressive technology entails incessant and often very rapid and startling changes of economic, political and ethical state; and such changes tend to keep the societies subjected to them in a chronically uncomfortable and unstable condition. Some day, perhaps, social scientists will be able to tell us what is the optimum rate of change, and what the optimum amount of it at any one time. For the present, Western societies remain at the mercy of their progressive technologies, to the intense discomfort of everybody concerned. Man as a moral, social and political being is sacrificed to *homo faber*, or man the smith, the inventor and forger of new gadgets.

And meanwhile, of course, technological unemployment is always with us; for every labor-saving device, every substitution of a new and more efficient technique for an older and less efficient one, results in a local and temporary diminution of the labor force. In the long run the persons displaced, as the result of technological advance, may find themselves reabsorbed by other industries or even (since increased efficiency results in lowered prices, greater demand and an expansion of production sufficient, in some cases, to offset the original technological unemployment) by the industry from which they were discharged. But what may happen in the long run is of little interest to propertyless persons who are compelled by hunger and the elements to do their living

[19]

exclusively in the short run. For such persons the chief consequence of progressive science is a chronic social and economic insecurity.

Here, as in an earlier paragraph, it is necessary to stress the fact that the progress of applied science is not the only causative factor involved. Mass unemployment and periodical slumps have a variety of interlocking causes—meteorological, financial and psychological causes as well as those connected with science and technology. Concerning the relative importance of these factors the experts are not yet agreed. Many theories of slumps and unemployment have been formulated, each of which emphasizes one of the known causative factors at the expense of all the rest. None of these theories is universally accepted; but all of them—and this, for our present purpose, is the important point—are agreed that technological unemployment is a reality and that the progress of applied science does in fact play an important part in creating that economic and social insecurity, which is the plague of modern industrial societies.

In the capitalist countries the nature of the monetary and financial systems has been such that, whenever a boom gets under way, the issuers of credit are compelled by the traditional rules of banking to withdraw credit and so to convert the boom into a slump. At the same time the owners of mass-producing industry are compelled by the rules of the game of profit making to practice what Thorstein Veblen used to call "capitalist sabotage"—in other words, they are compelled by the necessity of making profits to prevent their managers from producing as many goods and at as cheap a rate as they are technically equipped to do. In both cases the result of following the traditional rules is an accentuation of the social and economic insecurity normally resulting from technological progress. State socialists hold that the remedy for these evils can be found only in the nationalization of banking, land and industry—in other words, in the complete and final centralization of economic as well as political power in the hands of the currently ruling politicians and their managers. But power is in its essence expansive, and cannot be curbed except by other powers of equal or at least comparable magnitude. Under a regime of state socialism there would be no power systems within a community capable of opposing any serious resistance to the politically and economically almighty executive. The political bosses and civil servants in control of the state would themselves be controlled by nothing stronger than a paper constitution. In cases where state socialism succeeds capitalist democracy by non-violent, constitutional means, the rules of the political game are likely to remain, in many respects, identical with those prevailing under the older regime. For as long as the new system is administered by men brought up under democratic traditions, the constitutional rules will probably be observed. But when these men are succeeded by a new generation, born and brought up in a society dominated by the omnipotent state, what then? Only the most ingenuously optimistic, the most willfully blind to the facts of history and psychology, can believe that paper guarantees of liberty—guarantees wholly unsupported by the realities of political and economic power—will be scrupulously respected by those who have known only the facts of governmental omnipotence on the one hand and, on the other, of mass dependence upon, and consequently subervience to, the state and its representatives.

We see, then, that technological progress results

in economic and social insecurity, and that this insecurity is greatly aggravated, in the capitalist countries,
by the necessity of abiding by the traditional rules of
private banking, financing and mass production. By
nationalizing, or at the least by rigidly controlling,
industry, agriculture and banking, the state could
probably get rid of periodical depressions and would
be in a position to mitigate, by financial and political
measures, the worst consequences of scientific progress. In this way the advantages of centralized finance,
mass-producing industry and quasi-industrial agriculture could be reconciled with social and economic
security for the masses. But everything has its price,
and it seems unlikely that security achieved in this
way could for long coexist with that liberty under
law which, as Action was never tired of insisting, is
the end of all political action, all social and economic
arrangements.

At the present time the horrors of insecurity, as
exemplified above all in mass unemployment, have
impressed themselves so deeply upon the popular
mind that, if offered the choice between liberty and
security, most people would almost unhesitatingly
vote for security. Similar situations have occurred

at other periods of history. Thus, in the years which witnessed the final disintegration of the Roman Empire, the insecurity of life and property was such that many hitherto free peasants and yeomen voluntarily made over their land and even their persons to the nearest great lord, in exchange for his protection. It was better, they felt, to be the serf or even the domestic slave of a powerful noble than to be free, but at the mercy of bandits, barbarians and the men-at-arms of other hereditary magnates. The sources of our present insecurity are not the same as were the sources of the insecurity of fifteen hundred years ago; but in both cases the reaction to insecurity is identical—namely, a general wish to exchange freedom for protection, independence for guaranteed subsistence in the service of the holders of great power. But great power invariably exercises a corrupting influence on those who wield it; and when, in due course, the tyranny of the bosses in control of the omnipotent state becomes unbearable, the masses who now pine for security will begin to pine even more ardently for liberty. That they will be able to extort liberty from a ruling minority equipped by science with the very latest in self-propelled flame-throwers and atomic missiles seems in the highest degree unlikely. It is in *satyagraha*, or nonviolent direct action, that the only hope of future revolutions resides. Meanwhile there is no question, in the contemporary world, of any popular movement in favor of liberty. On the contrary, the masses are everywhere clamoring for ever greater governmental control of everything. Nor are these demands exclusively confined to the masses. The owners and managers of the various capitalist systems of production are also victims of the general insecurity. They too would like a measure of government control— enough control to guarantee profits, but not so much, of course, as to constitute expropriation or nationalization.

Is there any way in which the material advantages of progressive technology can be combined not only with security, but also with freedom? My own view, which is essentially that of the Decentralists, is that, so long as the results of pure science are applied for the purpose of making our system of mass-producing and mass-distributing industry more expensively elaborate and more highly specialized, there can be nothing but ever greater centralization of power in ever fewer hands. And the corollary of this centralization of economic and political power is the progressive loss by the masses of their civil liberties, their personal independence and their opportunities for self-government. But here we must note that there is nothing in the results of disinterested scientific research which makes it inevitable that they should be applied for the benefit of centralized finance, industry and government. If inventors and technicians so chose, they could just as well apply the results of pure science for the purpose of increasing the economic self-sufficiency and consequently the political independence of small owners, working either on their own or in co-operative groups, concerned not with mass distribution, but with subsistence and the supply of a local market. The sabbath was made for man, not man for the sabbath; and the same is true of applied science. Human beings have certain physical and psychological wants. They require food, clothing and shelter; and, for moral and mental health, they need to be given the opportunity to develop their latent potentialities to the fullest degree compatible with the freedom and well-being of others. And beyond these primary psychological needs lies man's spiritual need—the need, in theological language, to achieve his Final End, which is the unitive knowledge of ultimate Reality, the realization that Atman and Brahman are one, that the body is a temple of the Holy Ghost, that Tao or the Logos is at once transcendent and immanent.

Now it seems pretty obvious that man's psychological, to say nothing of his spiritual, needs cannot be fulfilled unless, first he has a fair measure of personal independence and personal responsibility within and toward a self-governing group, unless, secondly, his work possesses a certain aesthetic value and human significance, and unless, in the third place, he is related to his natural environment in some organic, rooted and symbiotic way. But in modern industrial societies vast numbers of men and women pass their whole lives in hideous cities, are wholly dependent for their livelihood upon a capitalistic or governmental boss, have to perform manual or clerical work that is repetitive, mechanical and intrinsically meaningless, are rootless, propertyless and entirely divorced from the world of nature, to which, as animals, they still belong and in which, as human beings, they might (if they were sufficiently humble and docile) discover the spiritual Reality in which the whole world, animate and inanimate, has its being. The reason for this dismal state of things is the progressive application of the results of pure science for the benefit of mass-producing and mass-distributing industry, and with the unconscious or conscious purpose of furthering centralization of power in finance, manufacture and government.

But now let us suppose that those who make it their business to apply the results of pure science to economic ends should elect to do so, not primarily for the benefit of big business, big cities and big government, but with the conscious aim of providing individuals with the means of doing profitable and intrinsically significant work, of helping men and women to achieve independence from bosses, so that they may become their own employers, or members of a self-governing, co-operative group working for subsistence and a local market. Suppose, I repeat, that this were henceforward to become the acknowledged purpose guiding the labors of inventors and engineers. Seconded by appropriate legislation, this differently orientated technological progress would result, not as at present in the further concentration of power and the completer subordination of the many to the few, but in a progressive decentralization of population, of accessibility of land, of ownership of the means of production, of political and economic power. Ralph Borsodi's studies have shown that mass-producing and mass-distributing methods are technologically justified in about one-third of the total production of goods. In regard to the remaining two-thirds, the economies effected by mass-production are offset by the increased costs involved in mass distribution over great areas, so that local production by individuals or co-operating groups, working for subsistence and a neighborhood market, is more economical than mass production in vast centralized factories. And to these economic advantages of decentralization must be added the social advantages of a more humanly satisfying life for more people, a greater measure of genuine self-governing democracy and a blessed freedom from the silly or penicious adult education provided by the mass producers of consumer goods through the medium of advertisements.

4. The continuous advance of science and technology has profoundly affected the prevailing mental

climate. The basic postulates of thought have been changed, so that what to our fathers seemed obviously true and important strikes us as either false or negligible and beside the point. Let us consider a few of the more significant of these changes and their effects upon the social and political life of our times.

a) Unlike art, science is genuinely progressive. Achievement in the fields of research and technology is cumulative; each generation begins at the point where its predecessor left off. Furthermore, the results of disinterested research were from the first applied in such a way that the upper and middle classes of all industrialized societies found themselves becoming steadily richer and richer. It was, therefore, only to be expected that the professional thinkers who sprang from these classes, and who were familiar with the methods and achievements of science, should have based upon the facts of technological and economic progress a general theory of human life. The world, they affirmed, was becoming materially, intellectually and morally better and better, and this amelioration was in some way inevitable. The theory of progress— a theory that soon became a dogma, indeed an axiom of popular thought—was novel and, from an orthodox Christian point of view, heretical. For orthodoxy, man was a fallen being. Humanity if not actively deteriorating, was statically bad, with a badness which only grace in co-operation with the individual's free will could possibly mitigate. In illustration of this, let us consider how the thirteenth century was regarded by those who lived through it, and how it is regarded by modern historians. For the latter it seems one of the most glorious periods in European history; the former were unanimous (as Professor Coulton has shown) in regarding it as an age of peculiar wickedness and manifest degeneracy. Even in the age of Queen Elizabeth thoughtful men were still talking of humanity's decline. It was not until the late seventeenth century (the age of the rise of modern science) that the note of bumptious self-congratulation began to be sounded, not until the eighteenth and nineteenth centuries that the dogma of inevitable progress became an unquestioned article of popular faith.

The belief in all-round progress is based upon the wishful dream that one can get something for nothing. Its underlying assumption is that gains in one field do not have to be paid for by losses in other

fields. For the ancient Greeks, *hubris*, or overween-
ing insolence, whether directed against the gods, or
one's fellow men, or nature, was sure to be followed,
sooner or later, in one way or another, by avenging
Nemesis. Unlike the Greeks, we of the twentieth
century believe that we can be insolent with im-
punity.

So intense is our faith in the dogma of inevitable
progress that it has survived two world wars and still
remains flourishing in spite of totalitarianism and
the revival of slavery, concentration camps and saturation bombing.

Faith in progress has affected contemporary political
life by reviving and popularizing, in an up-to-date,
pseudo-scientific and this-worldly form, the old Jew-
ish and Christian apocalypticism. A glorious destiny
awaits mankind, a coming Golden Age, in which
more ingenious gadgets, more grandiose plans and
more elaborate social institutions, will somehow have
created a race of better and brighter human beings.
Man's Final End is not in the eternal timeless Now,
but in a not too distant utopian future. In order to
secure the peace and happiness of their great-great-
grandchildren, the masses ought to accept and their

rulers need feel no qualms in imposing, any amount of war and slavery, of suffering and moral evil, in the present. It is a highly significant fact that all modern dictators, whether of the Right or of the Left, talk incessantly about the golden Future, and justify the most atrocious acts here and now, on the ground that they are means to that glorious end. But the one thing we all know about the future is that we are completely ignorant of what is going to happen, and that what does in fact happen is often very different from what we anticipated. Consequently any faith based upon hypothetical occurrences a long time hence must always, in the very nature of things, be hopelessly unrealistic. In practice, faith in the bigger and better future is one of the most potent enemies to present liberty; for rulers feel themselves justified in imposing the most monstrous tyrannies on their subjects for the sake of the wholly imaginary fruits which these tyrannies are expected (only an implicit faith in progress can say why) to bear some time, let us say, in the twenty-first or twenty-second century.

b) As theory, pure science is concerned with the reduction of diversity to identity. As a praxis, scientific research proceeds by simplification. These habits of scientific thought and action have, to a certain extent, been carried over into the theory and practice of contemporary politics. Where a centralized authority undertakes to make plans for an entire society, it is compelled by the bewildering complexity of the given facts to follow the example of the scientific experimenter, who arbitrarily simplifies his problem in order to make it manageable. In the laboratory this is a sound and entirely justifiable procedure. But when applied to the problems of human society, the process of simplification is a process, inevitably, of restraint and regimentation, of curtailment of liberty and denial of individual rights. This reduction of human diversity to a military and quasi-mechanical identity is achieved by propaganda, by legal enactments and, if necessary, by brute force—by the imprisonment, exile or liquidation of those persons, or those classes, who persist in their perverse desire to remain themselves and are obstinate in their reluctance to conform to the pattern which the political and economic bosses find it, at the moment, most convenient to impose. Philosophically, this ironing out of individual idiosyncrasies is held to be respectable,

[34]

because it is analogous to what is done by scientists, when they arbitrarily simplify an all too complex reality, so as to make nature comprehensible in terms of a few general laws. A highly organized and regimented society, whose members exhibit a minimum of personal peculiarities, and whose collective behavior is governed by a single master plan imposed from above, is felt by the planners and even (such is the power of propaganda) by the planees to be more "scientific," and therefore better, than a society of independent, freely co-operating and self-governing individuals.

c) The first step in this simplification of reality, without which (since human minds are finite and nature is infinite) scientific thought and action would be impossible, is a process of abstraction. Confronted by the data of experience, men of science begin by leaving out of account all those aspects of the facts which do not lend themselves to measurement and to explanation in terms of antecedent causes rather than of purpose, intention and values. Pragmatically they are justified in acting in this odd and extremely arbitrary way; for by concentrating exclusively on the measurable aspects of such elements of experience as can be explained in terms of a causal system they have been able to achieve a great and ever increasing control over the energies of nature. But power is not the same thing as insight and, as a representation of reality, the scientific picture of the world is inadequate, for the simple reason that science does not even profess to deal with experience as a whole, but only with certain aspects of it in certain contexts. All this is quite clearly understood by the more philosophically minded men of science. But unfortunately some scientists, many technicians and most consumers of gadgets have lacked the time and the inclination to examine the philosophical foundations and background of the sciences. Consequently they tend to accept the world picture implicit in the theories of science as a complete and exhaustive account of reality; they tend to regard those aspects of experience, which scientists leave out of account, because they are incompetent to deal with them, as being somehow less real than the aspects which science has arbitrarily chosen to abstract from out of the infinitely rich totality of given facts. Because of the prestige of science as a source of power, and because of the general neglect of philosophy, the popular *Weltan-*

schauung of our times contains a large element of what may be called "nothing-but" thinking. Human beings, it is more or less tacitly assumed, are nothing but bodies, animals, even machines; the only really real elements of reality are matter and energy in their measurable aspects; values are nothing but illusions that have somehow got themselves mixed up with our experience of the world; mental happenings are nothing but epiphenomena, produced by and entirely dependent upon physiology; spirituality is nothing but wish fulfillment and misdirected sex; and so on. The political consequences of this "nothing-but" philosophy are clearly apparent in that widespread indifference to the values of human personality and human life, which are so characteristic of the present age. Within the past thirty years, this indifference has expressed itself in a number of dangerous and disquieting ways. We have witnessed, first of all, the wholesale revival of slavery in its worst and most inhuman forms—slavery imposed upon political heretics living under the various dictatorships, slavery imposed upon whole classes of conquered populations, slavery imposed upon prisoners of war. Next, we note the increasing indiscriminateness of slaughter during wartime. Area bombing, saturation bombing, rocket bombing, bombing by atomic missiles—the indiscriminateness has steadily increased throughout the second World War, until now no nation even makes a pretense of observing the traditional distinction between civilians and combatants, innocent and guilty, but all devote themselves methodically and scientifically to general massacre and wholesale destruction. Other practical consequences of our "nothing-but" philosophies of life are the employment by civilized people, with a high standard of scientific and technological training, of torture, human vivisection and the systematic starvation of entire populations. And finally there is the phenomenon of forced migration—the removal at the point of the bayonet of millions of men, women and children from their homes to other places, where most of them will die of hunger, exposure and disease.

Unrealistic beliefs tend to result in foolish or morally evil actions; and such wrong beliefs cannot be got rid of, except by teaching right, or at least less erroneous, beliefs. If the ministers of the various sects and religions would abandon sentimentality and superstition, and devote themselves to teaching their flocks that the Final End of man is not in the unknowable utopian future, but in the timeless eternity of the Inner Light, which every human being is capable, if he so desires, of realizing here and now, then the myth of progress would lose its harmfulness as a justifier of present tyranny and wrongdoing. If scientists and technicians could be persuaded to read, for example, the essays in Edward Carpenter's *Civilization, Its Cause and Cure,* together with Professor Burtt's *Metaphysical Foundations of Modern Science* and the speculative writings of Sir Arthur Eddington, the disastrous notion that the contemporary scientific world picture is a complete representation of reality, and the no less disastrous habit of "nothing-but" evaluations of social and psychological facts might perhaps be eliminated, to the great advantage of suffering humanity. But *quis custodiet custodes?*—who is going to guard the guardians of our civilization, and who is going to teach its teachers? Our basic trouble is that, in spite of everything that has happened, everybody thinks he is right. In the past, despots committed the crimes that despots always do commit—but committed them with a conscience that was sometimes distinctly uneasy. They had been

[39]

brought up as Christians, as Hindus, as Moslems or Buddhists, and in the depths of their being they knew that they were doing wrong, because what they were doing was contrary to the teachings of their religion. Today the political boss has been brought up in our more enlightened and scientific environment. Consequently he is able to perpetrate his outrages with a perfectly clear conscience, convinced that he is acting for humanity's highest good—for is he not expediting the coming of the glorious future promised by Progress? is he not tidying up a messily individualistic society? is he not doing his utmost to substitute the wisdom of experts for the foolishness of men and women who want to do what they think (how erroneously, since of course they are not experts!) is best for them? And then there are the pastors and the schoolmasters. They have their Ph.D.'s and their D.D.'s, their academic positions and their cures of souls, their habits of authority and their high perches in the pulpit or on the lecture platform. Why should they change their long-established habits and the hallowed traditions of the organizations, of which they are the living pillars? The most important lesson of history, it has been said, is that nobody ever learns history's lessons. The enormous catastrophes of recent years have left the survivors thinking very much as they thought before. A horde of Bourbons, we return to what we call peace, having learned nothing and forgotten nothing—forgotten nothing, except, of course, the causes of war, which (whatever our intentions and our well-worded ideals) we do everything in our power to perpetuate.

IN A WORLD where the concentration of economic power is advantageous to the ruling minority, it is only natural that the results of disinterested scientific research should be applied in such a way as to foster large-scale mass production and mass distribution. And in a world where nationalism is taken for granted, and where the values of nationalism are held to be supreme, it is only natural that these same results should be applied to the end of producing and continually improving the instruments of war. Because it paid them to do so, men of science, inventors and engineers have worked to build up a system of centralized industry; and because, as nationalists, they thought it was their duty (and also, it must be added, because the duty was often a very profitable one), they have worked to produce such marvels of technological ingenuity as tanks, bombers, flamethrowers and atomic missiles.

"Nationality," wrote Lord Acton in 1862, "does not aim either at liberty or prosperity, both of which it sacrifices to the imperative necessity of making the nation the mould and measure of the state. Its course will be marked with material as well as moral ruin." Acton's prophecy is still in the terrible process of fulfillment. The material havoc wrought by applied science in the service of nationalism is such that it will take a generation to repair the damage. For many millions of men, women and especially children, the moral ruin caused by the war is irreparable; to the end of their lives they are doomed to remain psychologically warped, crippled and stunted. And these, of course, are not the only gifts of the nationalism, which (having repudiated all belief in the fatherhood of God and the brotherhood of man) we have set up as our idolatrous religion. The world is parceled out into some fifty-odd administrative units, calling themselves nations. In each of these nations there is a state religion—namely, the worship of the nation regarded as the supreme value, or God. To be a worshiper of one of the fifty-odd national Molochs is, necessarily and automatically, to be a crusader against the worshipers of all the other national Molochs. Nationalism leads to moral ruin because it denies universality, denies the existence of a single God, denies the value of the human being as a human being; and because, at the same time, it affirms exclusiveness, encourages vanity, pride and self-satisfaction, stimulates hatred and proclaims the necessity and the rightness of war. The fatal consequences of nationalism have been demonstrated again and again in the course of history. Consider, for example, the civilization of ancient Greece—the highest, in many respects, ever achieved in the Western world. After only a brief life it perished, self-destroyed by nationalism. Each city-state worshiped itself and consequently hated and despised its neighbors. The Greek world of the great poets, artists and philosophers was chronically in a state of civil war. In the end it bled to death, the victim of idolatrous and separatist patriotism. Fortunately, the Macedonians were at hand to take over.

The modern world differs from that of ancient Greece in degree and scale, not in kind. What separatist patriotism did for the inhabitants of a few thousand square miles in the eastern Mediterranean, it is doing today for the population of the entire planet. As Athens and Sparta died of idolatry and flag waving and jingoism, so we shall die of idolatry and flag waving and jingoism. But whereas the technologists at the service of the various Greek nationalisms had got no further than chariots and javelins, the technologists at the service of our fifty-odd self-worshiping administrative units have given us bombers that can fly nonstop for eight thousand miles, incendiaries that nobody can put out and atomic missiles that are guaranteed to do to whole cities what a quart of boiling water does to an ants' nest.

"Lead us not into temptation." The presence of this phrase in the Lord's Prayer reveals its author's profoundly realistic appreciation of human nature. Why should we pray that we may not be led into temptation? For the excellent reason that, as all experience proves, whenever temptations to evil are sufficiently strong and sufficiently frequent, men and women generally succumb to them. The existence of powerful armaments constitutes for their possessors a standing temptation to resort to violence. *Si vis bellum, para bellum*: and when the preparations for war are carried on with all the resources of progressive science and technology, the temptations to aggression, to the defense or consolidation of legitimate interests, to the realization of a manifest destiny (the names and justifications vary, but the nature of the consequent war remains the same), becomes progressively more intense, until at some critical moment—the moment when nation X feels certain of being, in some strategically significant way, better armed than nations Y and Z—it turns into a categorical imperative, a divine command to go to war for the greater glory of the nation-god. Nor is this the only temptation to present itself. Recent progress in the applied science of armament making has been a progress in the development of weapons that will destroy more indiscriminately at greater distances. High explosives and incendiaries, the heavy bomber and the jet-propelled robot plane, the rocket and finally the atomic missile—taken together these constitute a powerful temptation to ignore the traditional rules of war and to obliterate wholesale entire civilian populations and their dwellings. To this temptation all the belligerents in the second World War succumbed. And so long as governments and manufacturers continue to subsidize research into the science and technology of armaments, these temptations will remain, irresistibly beckoning to nationalistic power lovers, just as drink and sex and money beckon to their respective addicts.

In recent months many persons have optimistically argued that the harnessing of atomic energy must (because that energy is so destructive) put an end to men's inveterate habit of making war. Similar arguments have been set forth in the past. Whenever progressive applied science has produced some strikingly more efficient instrument of slaughter, hopes have been voiced, and facts and figures marshaled to prove, that henceforward war would be too expensive in life, suffering and money to be worth waging. Nevertheless wars have still been fought. Methods of defense against the new destructive weapon are devised and yet more efficient instruments of counterattack are invented. Advances in technology do not abolish the institution of war; they merely modify its manifestations. In the present instance it seems quite possible that there may be no defense against atomic missiles. But this does not necessarily presage the end of warfare. The collective mentality of nations—the mentality which reasonable adults have to adopt, when making important decisions in the field of international politics—is that of a delinquent boy of fourteen, at once cunning and childish, malevolent and silly, maniacally egotistical, touchy and acquisitive, and at the same time ludicrously boastful and vain. When the issues involved are of no great weight, the adults in control of a nation's policy are permitted, by the rules of the curious game they are playing, to behave like adults. But as soon as important economic interests or national prestige is involved, this grown-up Jekyll retires and his place is taken by an adolescent Hyde, whose ethical standards are those of a boy gangster and whose *Weltanschauung* seems to have been formed by a study of Houston Stewart Chamberlain and the more sanguinary comic strips. And let us remember that this same delinquent boy who, concealed in the middle-aged body of a politician, decrees that millions shall do and suffer the utmost in scientifically organized malice, resides within us all, ready and waiting, whenever some crisis makes us forget our surface rationality and idealism, to come out into the open. To this boy gangster in our midst, the natural reaction to the atom bomb is not an impulse to put an end to war by getting rid of its causes in nationalism, economic rivalry and the craving for power. Rather it is an impulse to make use of the new powers provided by science for the purpose of establishing world dominion for his particular gang. It is a highly significant fact that people love to talk about a war to end war, or a war to preserve democracy; they do not love to talk about peace to end war, or self-governing democracy (which is the polar antithesis of militarism) to preserve democracy. Like the adult, with whom he is associated, the nationalistic boy-gangster is frightened of what atomic power may do to him and his world. Nevertheless he continues to think in terms of gang rivalry and his own supremacy. "If," he argues, "our gang can get its scientists to perfect the rocket and the atom bomb, if it can get its manufacturers to produce enough plutonium and uranium 235, to build enough launching ramps and robot planes and V2's, then all that need be done is to press a few buttons and bang! the war to end war will be over, and I shall be the boss of the whole planet." Because of the boy gangster in every Foreign Office, every war department and every private home, we may expect that, in the years immediately ahead of us all the (technologically speaking) advanced nations will spend vast sums upon armament research and the manufacture of new weapons capable of more indiscriminate destruction at ever greater distances. This research will be secret—an affair of "Manhattan Projects" and "Tube Alloys"—and much of the manufacture will be carried on at the bottom of mines and caverns. And at some moment—unless, by a miracle, Jekyll should contrive to get the upper hand—the temptation to press those buttons will become irresistible; the juvenile delinquent in some Ministry for Foreign Affairs will call up his colleague at the Ministry of National Defense and bang! the war to make the world yet safer for delinquency will have begun.

In discussing the possibility of abolishing war, another important point to be remembered is that the preparation for war and sometimes even war itself are things which a highly centralized government finds very useful for its own totalitarian purposes. Thus, peacetime conscription is always justified on the ground that it constitutes an insurance against war, or at least against defeat in war. In actual fact, of course, nations which have adopted peacetime conscription have fought just as many wars as they fought before adopting it, and have suffered just as many defeats. The real, the unavowed reason for peacetime conscription must be sought in the all too natural desire of a powerful, centralized government to regiment and control its subjects by placing them, actually or potentially, under martial law and by arrogating to itself the right, whenever it so desires (as, for example, during an inconvenient strike), to call them to the colors. In these days of atomic weapons, mass armies would seem to have become something of an anachronism. Nevertheless no country which imposed peacetime conscription in the past shows any inclination to relax its grip upon the masses of its people. Moreover in countries where peacetime conscription was previously unheard-of there are many high military and civilian officials who advocate the imposition of permanent military servitude upon the masses.

There is also another way in which the preparation for war is useful to the holders of centralized political power. When things go badly at home, when popular discontent becomes inconveniently articulate, it is always possible, in a world where war making remains an almost sacred habit, to shift the people's attention away from domestic to foreign and military affairs. A flood of xenophobic or imperialistic propaganda is released by the government-controlled instruments of persuasion, a "strong policy" is adopted toward some foreign power, an appeal for "national unity" (in other words, unquestioning obedience to the ruling oligarchy) is launched, and at once it becomes unpatriotic for anybody to voice even the most justifiable complaints against mismanagement or oppression. It is difficult to see how any highly centralized government could afford to dispense with militarism and the threat of foreign war. This constitutes yet another argument for the division and dispersal of power, the de-institutionalizing of politics and economics and the substitution, wherever possible, of regional cooperative self help for centralized mass production and mass distribution, and of regional, co-operative self-government for state intervention and state control.

Finally we have to consider the part played by militarism in solving those problems of economic and social insecurity, which, as we have seen, are the curse of a technologically progressive society. The great depression of the 1930's was accompanied, in all industrialized countries, by mass unemployment. This fearful social sickness was treated in a variety of ways. Thus, in Great Britain an ambitious housing program was launched; in the United States the

Roosevelt administration resorted to public works, "pump priming" and restriction of agricultural output with a view to raising prices. These measures were only partially successful. The numbers of the unemployed were reduced, but unemployment was by no means eliminated. Complete success came only when Hitler embarked upon large-scale rearmament. As though by magic, unemployment was banished— first from Germany and, later, as other countries took fright and joined the armament race, throughout the rest of the industrialized world. A cure had been found for the insecurity, which is the fruit of scientific and technological progress, when it is at the service of centralized finance. But the price of the temporary cure was death and destruction, and the last state of all the nations concerned was incomparably worse than the first. Nevertheless it seems quite possible that wholesale rearmament may, at some future date, again be used to palliate the symptoms of unemployment.

It should be remarked that, under the present dispensation, armaments are the only goods that are given away without consideration of costs or profits. Modern war is, among other things, a competition among nations as to which can hand out, free, gratis and for nothing, the largest amount of capital goods in the shortest time. These capital goods are all maleficent and unproductive; but the thought occurs to one that something resembling wartime prosperity might be made permanent if there were more giving away at cost, or even for nothing, and less selling at a profit and paying of interest. Were this to happen, we should have a centralized financing, mass production and mass distribution, combined with a political system approximating state socialism. That this arrangement would in some ways be preferable to the present dispensation seems likely enough. But we must remember that any government enjoying a monopoly of political and economic power is exposed to almost irresistible temptations to tyranny. There has never been a time when too much power did not corrupt its possessors and there is absolutely no reason to suppose that, in this respect, the future behavior of human beings will be in any way different from their behavior in the past and at the present time. The arguments for the limitation and decentralization of power remain valid, even when that power is concentrated in the hands of an oligarchy of socialists—a phrase which is actually a contradiction in terms; for, to quote Mr. Middleton Murry: "Socialism by autocracy or oligarchy is not socialism, or anything like it." It is just benevolent despotism; and there is nothing in the record of history to justify us in the belief that any benevolent despotism will for long retain its benevolence. The appetite for power grows with every successive satisfaction of that most alluring and pernicious of all the lusts. Against the temptations to abuse power there is no armor except sanctity. But since very few human beings are prepared to pay the price of sanctity and very few saints desire power, mere common sense demands that the amount of power wielded by any individual or organization of individuals should be strictly limited and that the principle of self-government (which is the principle of the division of power, the balancing and compromise of independent forces) should be applied, and applied to the extreme practicable limit, in every field of human activity. This entails the de-institutionalization of many political and economic procedures, which are at present planned from above by the functionaries of private capitalism or the national state. In present circumstances it is most unlikely that this highly desirable process of decentralization and de-institutionalization will be carried out. By the education they have received in schools and, later, at the hands of the writers of advertising copy and political propaganda, the great majority of men and women have been conditioned to believe that progressive institutionalization, controlled by private capitalists, or the state, or both together, is an intrinsically beneficent thing and at the same time an inevitable and quasi-natural development. Those who have a reasoned belief in the current centralist philosophy and those, much more numerous, who take it for granted by an act of implicit faith, cannot be expected to look with anything but suspicion on the ideas of de-institutionalization, self-help and self-government. What is needed is a restatement of the Emersonian doctrine of self-reliance—a restatement, not abstract and general, but fully documented with an account of all the presently available techniques for achieving independence within a localized, co-operative community. These techniques are of many kinds—agricultural techniques designed to supply the basic social unit, the family, with its staple food supply; mechanical techniques for the production of many consumer goods for a local market; financial techniques, such as those of the credit union, by means of which individuals can borrow money without increasing the power of the state or of commercial banks; legal techniques, through which a community can protect itself against the profiteer who speculates in land values, which he has done nothing whatever to increase. At present this documented and practical restatement of an old doctrine is being made by such men as Wilfred Wellock in England, as Ralph Borsodi and the writers who contribute to *Free America* in the United States. In the enormous bellowing chorus of advertisers singing the praises of centralized mass-producing and mass-distributing industry, and of Left-wing propogandists singing the praises of the omnipotent state, these few isolated voices have some difficulty in making themselves heard. If it were not for the fact that, in the past, apparently negligible movements, originating among individuals without any political power, have yet exercised a prodigious influence over mankind, there would be reason for discouragement. But fortunately it is not impossible that the presently tiny piece of decentralist leaven may end by leavening the whole huge lump of contemporary society.

It is not impossible, I repeat; but it must be added

that, so long as the nations stick to their ancient habit of war making, it is highly improbable. For the nature of modern war is such that it cannot be successfully waged by any nation which does not possess a highly developed, not to say hypertrophied, capital-goods industry supplemented by a mass-producing consumer-goods industry capable of rapid expansion and conversion for wartime needs. Furthermore it cannot be waged successfully, except by nations which can mobilize their entire man-power and woman-power in universal military or industrial conscription. But universal conscription is most easily imposed where large numbers of the population are rootless, propertyless and entirely dependent for their livelihood upon the state or upon large-scale private employers. Such persons constitute that dream of every militaristic dictator—a "fluid labor force," which can be shifted at will from one place or one unskilled job to another place or job. Again, big centralized corporations and their wage-earning employees can be taxed much more easily and profitably than small-scale farmers working primarily for subsistence and only secondarily for cash, or than independent or co-operative producers of commodities for a localized

market. For this reason anything like a popular movement in the direction of decentralization could hardly
be tolerated by any government desirous of becoming
or remaining a "great power." It may be argued that
the bomber and the rocket may force all nations to
undertake a geographical dispersion of industries; but
such dispersion can take place without any real decentralization of political and economic power, any
real increase of individual independence from governmental or capitalist control, or any expansion of
the present area of voluntary co-operation, self government and de-institutionalized activity.

"Science" is an abstract word, and when we are
trying to think about concrete political and economic
problems, it is best to talk concretely, not of science
but of the people who work in the various scientific
fields, from the fields of uncontaminated theory and
disinterested research into basic problems to those of
applied science and technology. Assuming that the
abolition of war is desirable, we proceed to ask our-
selves how scientific workers can help to achieve this
end.

1. As individuals or in organized groups, scientific
workers can take three kinds of action against war.

There is, first, the possibility of negative action in the form of a refusal, on conscientious grounds, to participate in work having as its purpose the killing, torture or enslavement of human beings. Christianity once insisted, and Buddhism still insists, upon the importance of "right livelihood." There are certain professions so intrinsically harmful that no individual ought to practice them. In the eyes of medieval Catholic theologians, for example, the profession of a moneylender or of a speculator was beyond the pale: they held that a man could not live by usury and the manipulation of the commodity markets, and still be regarded as a Christian. Similarly, for Buddha and his followers, a man could not be regarded as a Buddhist, if he made his living by the manufacture of arms or intoxicants. Men of science and technologists would do well, as individuals and in their national and international organizations, to consider the problem of right livelihood in its relation to their own contemporary activities. It is possible to work on the development of instruments of ever more indiscriminate slaughter and to remain—not a good Christian or a good Buddhist; for in scientific and technological circles religion is now out of fashion—

but a good human being? Is it possible to go on believing that one is working for the good of mankind, while applying the results of disinterested research in ways which demonstrably increase the power of the ruling capitalist or governmental minority at the expense of personal liberty and local and professional self-government? These and similar questions need to be asked and carefully answered by scientific workers—asked and answered, if possible, on the level of their international organizations. Meanwhile it is to be hoped and perhaps expected that a certain number of individual scientists and technicians will take the negative stand against war and the centralization of power which is war's inevitable accompaniment, by refusing to collaborate in any project whose purpose is the destruction or enslavement of human beings.

2. Negative action is good so far as it goes, but it needs to be supplemented by action of a positive and constructive kind. Such positive action may be classified under two heads: (a) action which takes its start in politics, to end in the field of science: and (b) action which takes its start in science, to end in politics.

[61]

In recent months several suggestions have been made for the political control, in the interests of humanity, of the activities of scientists and technologists. Thus, in the course of an interesting two-day debate in the House of Lords (May 29 and 30, 1945) Lord Vansittart urged the necessity of subjecting all German laboratories, whether attached to universities or supported by the state or by private industrialists, to strict supervision over a long term of years. Only in this way, he claimed, could the danger of a war of revenge, waged with new "secret weapons," be avoided. More realistically, Lord Brabazon proposed that this supervision of scientific developments should not be confined exclusively to the defeated nations— nations whose opportunities for the large-scale manufacture of new weapons would, for many years at least, be small. His suggestion was that, under the final peace treaties, an international committee of inspection should be constituted, having authority to enter laboratories and factories in any part of the world. In Lord Brabazon's view, the only alternative to such a scheme of international inspection would be an armament race between Britain and the United States on the one hand and the rest of the world on the other. By intensive research the Anglo-Saxon group might hope to obtain the lead in such a race, and so discourage attack by other powers. Lord Brabazon's speech was made before the dropping of the first atomic bomb. As things now stand, the United States and Britain already possess an enormous lead in the postwar armament race. For a few years they may keep that lead. Then other nations (unless, of course, they are previously blown to bits by the present possessors of the bomb, or unless reason, surrender of absolute sovereignty and world government come to replace nationalism) will be supplied by their scientists with the same or even better methods for manufacturing atomic missiles. Meanwhile the desirability of an international inspectorate charged with preserving humanity from the triumphs of science is even greater now than it was before Hiroshima. The existence of an international inspectorate would involve the adoption of another security measure, advocated in the course of the same debate by Lord Strabolgi—namely, the pooling of all scientific discoveries considered by competent experts to be actually or potentially a danger to mankind.

Similar suggestions have been made on the other

side of the Atlantic, and it now (winter, 1945) remains to be seen whether, and to what extent, the United Nations will act upon them. Meanwhile Messrs. Truman, Attlee and King have decided to keep such secrets as their scientists and engineers still possess until "enforcible safeguards" against their use for destructive purposes can be devised. What is to be the nature of those "enforcible safeguards"? As yet, it would seem, nobody has any very clear idea. In principle, the proposals for a pooling of dangerous knowledge and for an international inspectorate are excellent; and, to some, the theory of an "international police force" seems attractive and even workable. But, alas, from principle to application and from theory to practice the road is long and hard. Two disturbing questions inevitably propound themselves. First, will the various national governments concerned agree to act upon these suggestions? Second, if they do agree, will they and the men of science they employ consent to play the game according to the internationally imposed rules? In attempting to answer these questions one must weigh the power of enlightened self-interest against the power of nationalistic passions and prejudices. Enlightened self-interest will unquestioningly vote for world government, international inspection and the pooling of information. But unfortunately, in some of the most important issues of life, human beings do not act from considerations of enlightened self-interest. If they did, we should now be living in something very like paradise. In the field of international politics, as we have seen, the gravest decisions are always taken, not by reasonable adults but by boy gangsters. Despite the lessons of Hiroshima and Nagasaki, it is quite possible that some national governments will refuse to allow their laboratories and factories to be inspected—and, of course, the refusal of even one government will entail the general abandonment of the scheme. Alternatively, the principle of international inspection will be accepted; but at first some and then (when suspicion has been aroused) all the governments concerned will conspire with the scientists in their employ to carry on research in caves or forests or mountain fastnesses, where no prying eye can see what they are up to. It may perhaps seem unlikely that workers trained in the methods of science should support their political bosses in machiations so manifestly senseless, as well as immoral.

But it is not because men have learned to behave rationally in the laboratory that they can be trusted to behave rationally toward foreigners and unpopular minorities, or even toward their own wives and children. Until a very few years ago the best scientific and technological education available was given in Germany; but most of the persons who received that education not only worked for the Nazi bosses, but believed in their doctrines and were swayed by the nationalistic passions which they so skillfully exploited. The case of Germany is not unique. In all countries nationalistic passions (of the same kind as were manifested in Germany, but at a somewhat lower level of intensity) are almost as common among scientists and technicians as in other classes of society. In spite of their training (perhaps, indeed, owing to the narrowly specialized character of that training, because of it), scientists and technicians are perfectly capable of the most dangerously irrational prejudice, nor are they immune to deceitful propaganda. The same men who reject as superstitious the belief in a transcendent and immanent spiritual Reality beyond and within phenomena, prove by their actions that they find no difficulty in worshiping as a supreme god whichever one of the world's fifty-odd nations they happen to belong to, and in accepting the infallibility of the local Foreign Office and the quasi-divinity of the local political boss. In view of all this we need not be surprised if the plans for an international inspectorate and the pooling of scientific knowledge should fail in practice to produce the good results expected of them.

b) We must now consider the specifically scientific action which might be taken by men of science and technicians with a view to diminishing the probability of war and so to increasing the sum of human liberty. Such action can only be taken on the plane of applied science. Basic research is essentially disinterested. Men undertake it because, in the words used by the boy Clerk Maxwell, they want to find out "what's the go" of things—to discover how nature works and how its parts are related within a causal system. What is subsequently done with the results of disinterested research is something which the researcher cannot foresee, and for which he is not responsible. Thus, Clerk Maxwell's own adult curiosity to find out the go of such things as light and magnetism led him to certain conclusions, and these conclusions have since been utilized by technicians for the development of instruments, which are now used, in the main, for the dissemination of maudlin drama, cigarette advertising, bad music and government-sponsored or capitalist-sponsored propaganda. Clerk Maxwell would probably have been horrified by all these uses of the radio, and he is, of course, in no way to blame for them. In practice, it would seem, basic research cannot be planned, except perhaps to the extent of subsidizing inquiry into branches of knowledge which, for whatever reason, appear to have been unduly neglected. If the facilities for research are supplied, men and women with an overpowering desire to find out the go of things will always be forthcoming to make use of them. The planning of scientific activity with a view to achieving certain predetermined political, social and economic ends must begin at the point where the results of disinterested research are applied to the solution of practical problems. Individually and through their professional organizations, scientists and technicians could do a great deal to direct that planning toward humane and reasonable ends.

In theory everyone agrees that applied science was

made for man and not man for applied science. In practice great masses of human beings have again and again been sacrificed to applied science. The conflict between science, as it has been applied up to the present, and human interests was clearly stated by Thorstein Veblen in his *Science in the Modern World*. In this essay Veblen distinguishes between what he calls the pragmatic and the scientific point of view. Pragmatically human beings know pretty well what is good for them, and have developed myths and fairy tales, proverbs and popular philosophies, behavior-patterns and moralities, in order to illustrate and embody their findings about life. The findings of science—especially of science as applied for the benefit of the holders of centralized economic and political power—are frequently in conflict with humanity's pragmatic values, and this conflict has been and still is the source of much unhappiness, frustration and bitterness. The enormous practical importance of the clash between scientific (or rather applied-scientific) values and pragmatic human values is stressed in an editorial which appeared in a recent issue (July 22, 1945) of the leading British scientific journal *Nature*. In maintaining industrial morals

[69]

"the central difficulty," writes the author of this article, "is essentially the inevitable opposition which develops between the scientific approach to the human problems of production and the political approach of the administrator, trained in the method of accommodation and compromise. The balancing of opinion and the compromise of different points of view, which is the essence of the political process, may be totally at odds with the scientific approach to questions of industrial management. What is required is not the surrender of scientific principles of established accuracy, or the ignoring of accepted fact, but the combination or integration of both the political and scientific approach in a solution which satisfies both the scientific and the psychological or political requirements."

Let us begin by noting that in any discussion of economic or political problems, the word "integration" is always a danger signal; for it is always tacitly assumed that the work of integration is carried out by somebody standing above the processes and persons to be integrated. In other words, whenever people call for "integration" they are always calling for the exercise of centralized governmental power and

[70]

for yet another extension of the process of institutionalization. But power is always corrupting, and
no human being or group of human beings is to be
trusted with too much of it for too long. When science is applied in such a way as to create a form of
production, which cannot be run efficiently without
coming into sharp conflict with fundamental human
values, and which therefore continually calls for the
intervention of a governmental authority having
power to "integrate" the conflicting persons and
points of view, it may be fairly presumed that the
application of the results of disinterested research
has been, humanly speaking, misguided and undesirable. Up to the present time applied science has
not been used mainly or primarily for the benefit of
humanity at large, or (to put the matter less ab-
stractly) for the benefit of individual men and women,
considered as personalities each one of which is capable, given suitable material and social conditions,
of a moral and spiritual development amounting, in
some cases, to a total transfiguration; rather man has
been used for applied science, for the technicians
who enjoy designing more and more complicated
gadgets, and for the financial and governmental in-

terests which profit by the centralization of power. If applied science is henceforward to be used for man, technicians and scientists will have to adopt a professional policy, consciously and deliberately designed to serve fundamental human needs and to forward the causes of peace and personal liberty. Such a policy could not be worked out in detail except by an international organization of scientific workers, highly trained in their respective fields, so that each could contribute his or her share of skill or information toward the realization of the common end—namely, the welfare, liberty and peace of the individuals composing the human race. It would be absurd for me to try to anticipate the findings of this hypothetical group of experts; but it is possible, without too much presumption, to indicate in a general way a few of the lines which their discussion would have to follow.

Humanity's primary requirement is a sufficiency of food; but it is primarily by considerations of power that the policies of national governments are at present dictated. The ruling minorities of the world invariably contrive to have enough, and (to judge by the disgusting descriptions of recent diplomatic banquets) more than enough, to eat; consequently they tend to take food for granted and to think first, and at times almost exclusively, in terms of the questions: Who shall bully whom? But the great majority of the men, women and children on this planet are in no position to take food for granted. Their first and often their exclusive concern is the next meal. The question as to who shall bully whom is of hardly more than academic interest to them. They would like, of course, to be left in peace to go their own way; but they know by bitter experience that, under the present dispensation, there will always be a ruling minority to order them about, to bully and badger them in the name of the divine Nation, the omniscient Party, the sacred Principles of this or that political doctrine. They are therefore unable to take much interest in the national and international policies, which are the prime concern of the well-fed power lovers at the top of the social lovers at the top of the social pyramid.

At the San Francisco Conference the only problems discussed were problems of power. The basic problem of mankind—the problem of getting enough to eat—was relegated to an obscure international committee on agriculture. And yet it is surely obvious that if genuine international agreement is ever to be reached and preserved, it must be an agreement with regard to problems which, first, are of vital interest to the great masses of humanity and which, second, are capable of solution without resort to war or the threat of war. The problems of power are primarily the concern of the ruling few, and the nature of power is essentially expansive, so that there is not the least prospect of power problems being solved, when one expanding system collides with another expanding system, except by means of organized, scientific violence or war. But war on the modern scale shatters the thin, precarious crust of civilization and precipitates vast numbers of human beings into an abyss of misery and slow death of moral apathy or positive and frenzied diabolism. If politicians were sincere in their loudly expressed desire for peace, they would do all they could to by-pass the absolutedly insoluble problems of power by concentrating all their attention, during international conferences and diplomatic discussions, on the one great problem which every member of the human race is concerned to solve—the one great problem which not only does not require military violence for its solution, but which, for the world at large, is wholly insoluble so long as the old games of militarism and power politics continue to be played. The first item on the agenda of every meeting between the representatives of the various nations should be: *How are all men, women and children to get enough to eat?*

It is fashionable nowadays to say that Malthus was wrong, because he did not foresee that improved methods of transportation can now guarantee that food surpluses produced in one area shall be quickly and cheaply transferred to another, where there is a shortage. But first of all, modern transportation methods break down whenever the power politicians resort to modern war, and even when the fighting stops they are apt to remain disrupted long enough to guarantee the starvation of millions of persons. And, secondly, no country in which population has outstripped the local food supply can, under present conditions, establish a claim on the surpluses of other countries without paying for them in cash or exports. Great Britain and the other countries in western Europe, which cannot feed their dense populations, have been able, in times of peace, to pay for the food they imported by means of the export of manufactured goods. But industrially backward India and China—countries in which Malthus' nightmare has come true with a vengeance and on the largest scale—produce few manufactured goods, consequently lack the means to buy from underpopulated areas the food they need. But when and if they develop mass-producing industries to the point at which they are able to export enough to pay for the food their rapidly expanding populations require, what will be the effect upon world trade and international politics? Japan had to export manufactured goods in order to pay for the food that could not be produced on the overcrowded home islands. Goods produced by workers with a low standard of living came into competition with goods produced by the better paid workers of the West, and undersold them. The West's retort was political and consisted of the imposition of high tariffs, quotas and embargoes. To these restrictions on her trade Japan's answer was the plan for creating a vast Asiatic empire at the expense of China and of the Western imperialist powers. The result was war. What will happen when India and China are as highly industrialized as prewar Japan and seek to exchange their low-priced manufactured goods for food, in competition with Western powers, whose standard of living is a great deal higher than theirs? Nobody can foretell the future; but undoubtedly the rapid industrialization of Asia (with equipment, let it be remembered, of the very latest and best postwar design) is pregnant with the most dangerous possibilities.

It is at this point that internationally organized scientists and technicians might contribute greatly to the cause of peace by planning a world-wide campaign, not merely for greater food production, but also (and this is the really important point) for regional self-sufficiency in food production. Greater food production can be obtained relatively easily by the opening up of the earth's vast subarctic regions at present almost completely sterile. Spectacular progress has recently been made in this direction by the agricultural scientists of the Soviet Union; and presumably what can be done in Siberia can also be done in northern Canada. Powerful ice-breakers are already being used to solve the problems of transportation by sea and river; and perhaps commercial submarines, specially equipped for traveling under the ice may in the future insure a regular service between arctic ports and the rest of the world. Any increase of the world's too scanty food supply is to be welcomed. But our rejoicings must be tempered by two considerations. First, the surpluses of food produced by the still hypothetical arctic granaries of Siberia and Canada will have to be transferred by ship, plane and rail to the overpopulated areas of the world. This means that no supplies would be available in wartime. Second, possession of food-producing arctic areas constitutes a natural monopoly, and this natural monopoly will not, as in the past, be in the hands of politically weak nations, such as Argentina and Australia, but will be controlled by the two great power systems of the postwar period—the Russian power system and the Anglo-American power system. That their monopolies of food surpluses will be used as weapons in the game of power politics seems more than probable. "Lead us not into temptation." The opening up of the Arctic will be undoubtedly a great good. But it will also be a great temptation for the power politicians—a temptation to exploit a natural monopoly in order to gain influence and finally control over hitherto independent countries, in which population has outstripped the food supply.

It would seem, then, that any scientific and technological campaign aimed at the fostering of international peace and political and personal liberty must, if it is to succeed, increase the total planetary food supply by increasing the various regional supplies to the point of self-sufficiency. Recent history makes it abundantly clear that nations, as at present constituted, are quite unfit to have extensive commercial dealings with one another. International trade has always, hitherto, gone hand in hand with war, imperialism and the ruthless exploitation of industrially backward peoples by the highly industrialized powers. Hence the desirability of reducing international trade to a minimum, until such time as nationalist passions lose their intensity and it becomes possible to establish some form of world government. As a first step in this direction, scientific and technical means must be found for making it possible for even the most densely populated countries to feed their inhabitants. The improvement of existing food plants and domestic animals; the acclimatization in hitherto inhospitable regions of plants that have proved useful elsewhere; the reduction of the present enormous wastes of food by the improvement of insect controls and the multiplication of refrigerating units; the more systematic exploitation of seas and lakes as sources of food; the development of entirely new foods, such as edible yeasts; the synthesizing of sugars as a food for such edible yeasts; the synthesizing of chlorophyll so as to make direct use of solar energy in food production— these are a few of the lines along which important advances might be made in a relatively short time.

Hardly less important than regional self-sufficiency in food is self-sufficiency in power for industry, agriculture and transportation. One of the contributing causes of recent wars has been international competition for the world's strictly localized sources of petroleum, and the current jockeying for position in the Middle East, where all the surviving great powers have staked out claims to Persian, Mesopotamian and Arabian oil, bodes ill for the future. Organized science could diminish these temptations to armed conflict by finding means for providing all countries, whatever their natural resources, with a sufficiency of power. Water power has already been pretty well exploited. Besides, over large areas of the earth's surface there are no mountains and therefore no sources of hydroelectric power. But across the plains where water stands almost still, the air often moves in strong and regular currents. Small windmills have been turning for centuries; but the use of large-scale wind turbines is still, strangely enough, only in the experimental stage. Until recently the direct use of solar power has been impracticable, owing to the technical difficulty of constructing suitable reflectors. A few months ago, however, it was announced that Russian engineers had developed a cheap and simple method for constructing paraboloid mirrors of large size, capable of producing superheated steam and even of melting iron. This discovery could be made to contribute very greatly to the decentralization of production and population and the creation of a new type of agrarian society making use of cheap and inexhaustible power for the benefit of individual small holders or self-governing, co-operative groups. For the peoples of such tropical countries as India and Africa the new device for directly harnessing solar power should be of enormous and enduring benefit —unless, of course, those at present possessing economic and political power should choose to build mass-producing factories around enormous mirrors, thus perverting the invention to their own centralistic purposes, instead of encouraging its small-scale use for the benefit of individuals and village communities. The technicians of solar power will be confronted with a clear-cut choice. They can work either for the completer enslavement of the industrially backward peoples of the tropics, or for their progressive liberation from the twin curses of poverty and servitude to political and economic bosses.

The storage of the potentialities of power is almost as important as the production of power. One of the most urgent tasks before applied science is the development of some portable source of power to replace petroleum—a most undesirable fuel from the political point of view, since deposits of it are rare and unevenly distributed over the earth's surface, thus constituting natural monopolies which, when in the hands of strong nations, are used to increase their strength at the expense of their neighbors and, when possessed by weak ones, are coveted by the strong and constitute almost irresistible temptations to imperialism and war. From the political and human point of view, the most desirable substitute for petroleum would be an efficient battery for storing the electric power produced by water, wind or the sun.

Further research into atomic structure may perhaps suggest new methods for the construction of such a battery.

Meanwhile it is possible that means may be devised, within the next few years, for applying atomic energy to the purposes of peace, as it is now being applied to those of war. Would not this technological development solve the whole problem of power for industry and transportation? The answer to this question may turn out to be simultaneously affirmative and negative. The problems of power may indeed be solved—but solved in the wrong way, by which I mean in a way favorable to centralization and the ruling minority, not for the benefit of individuals and co-operative, self-governing groups. If the raw material of atomic energy must be sought in radio-active deposits, occurring sporadically, here and there, over the earth's surface, then we have natural monopoly with all its undesirable political consequences, all its temptations to power politics, war, imperialistic aggression and exploitation. But of course it is always possible that other methods of releasing atomic energy may be discovered—methods that will not involve the use of uranium. In this case there will be no natural monopoly. But the process of releasing atomic energy will always be a very difficult and complicated affair, to be accomplished only on the largest scale and in the most elaborately equipped factories. Furthermore, whatever political agreements may be made, the fact that atomic energy possesses unique destructive potentialities will always constitute a temptation to the boy gangster who lurks within every patriotic nationalist. And even if a world government should be set up within a fairly short space of time, this will not necessarily guarantee peace. The Pax Romana was a very uneasy affair, troubled at almost every imperial death by civil strife over the question of succession. So long as the lust for power persists as a human trait—and in persons of a certain kind of physique and temperament this lust is overmasteringly strong—no political arrangement, however well contrived, can guarantee peace. For such men the instruments of violence are as fearfully tempting as are, to others, the bodies of women. Of all instruments of violence, those powered by atomic energy are the most decisively destructive; and for power lovers, even under a system of world government, the temptation to resort to these all too simple and effective means for gratifying their lust will be great indeed. In view of all this, we must conclude that atomic energy is, and for a long time is likely to remain, a source of industrial power that is, politically and humanly speaking, in the highest degree undesirable.

It is not necessary in this place, nor am I competent, to enter any further into the hypothetical policy of internationally organized science. If that policy is to make a real contribution toward the maintenance of peace and the spread of political and personal liberty, it must be patterned throughout along the decentralist lines laid down in the preceding discussion of the two basic problems of food and power. Will scientists and technicians collaborate to formulate and pursue some such policy as that which has been adumbrated here? Or will they permit themselves, as they have done only too often in the past, to become the conscious or unconscious instruments of militarists, imperialists and a ruling oligarchy of capitalistic or governmental bosses? Time alone will show. Meanwhile, it is to be hoped that all concerned will carefully consider a suggestion made by Dr. Gene Weltfish in the September, 1945, issue of the

[85]

Scientific Monthly. Before embarking upon practice, all physicians swear a professional oath—the oath of Hippocrates—that they will not take improper advantage of their position, but always remember their responsibilities toward suffering humanity. Technicans and scientists, proposes Dr. Weltfish, should take a similar oath in some such words as the following: "I pledge myself that I will use my knowledge for the good of humanity and against the destructive forces of the world and the ruthless intent of men; and that I will work together with my fellow scientists of whatever nation, creed or color for these our common ends."

Set in Linotype Baskerville
Format by A. W. Rushmore
Manufactured by The Haddon Craftsmen
Published by HARPER & BROTHERS
New York and London